# The Royal Horticultural Society
# Address Book
## Botanical Drawings

## JOHN LINDLEY (1799 – 1865)

*Commentary by Brent Elliott*

**TED SMART**

Frances Lincoln Limited
4 Torriano Mews
Torriano Avenue
London NW5 2RZ

www.franceslincoln.com

The Royal Horticultural Society Address Book
Botanical Drawings

British Library cataloguing-in-publication data
A catalogue record for this book is available from the British Library

ISBN 0-7112-2137-5

Printed in Hong Kong

First Frances Lincoln edition 1998
This edition produced for The Book People Limited, Hall Wood Avenue, Haydock, St Helens WA11 9UL

*Front cover*

*Myosotis azorica*, the Azorean Forget-me-not, a hand-retouched chromolithograph by Louis-Aristide-Léon Constans (*fl.* 1830s–1860s), from the third volume of *Paxton's Flower Garden* (1852–1853) by John Lindley and Joseph Paxton

*Title page*

*Crocus pusillus* (now *C. biflorus*), a hand-coloured engraving after a drawing by Miss S. A. Drake (*fl.* 1820s–1840s), from the 23rd volume of the *Botanical Register* (1837), edited by John Lindley

# JOHN LINDLEY

## 1799–1865

John Lindley was born on 5 February 1799. His father was George Lindley, a nurseryman at Catton, near Norwich, whose book *The Orchard and Kitchen Garden* John later edited for publication. In 1818 he went to London and, through his friend William Hooker, found employment helping with the arrangement of Robert Brown's herbarium in Sir Joseph Banks's library. After Banks's death in 1820, Lindley was hired by William Cattley of Barnet to publish the *Collectanea botanica*, a series of illustrations of plants from Cattley's collection.

In 1821, Lindley began working for the Horticultural Society as an artist, his specific brief being to draw roses. He excelled, and in the following year was appointed Assistant Secretary at the Society's new garden at Chiswick, his duties being 'to have superintendence over the collection of plants, and all other matters in the Garden'. It was at Chiswick that Lindley established shows with competitive classes, to which the origins of the modern flower show can be traced. It was also during this period that he wrote his first paper to be published in the Society's *Transactions*: 'A sketch of the principal tropical fruits which are likely to be worth cultivating in England for the dessert' (volume V, 1821–1822). In 1827 he was elevated to the position of Assistant Secretary to the Society as a whole, with duties at both Chiswick and its London offices. As Assistant Secretary he also acted as the editor of the Society's publications – first the *Transactions*, and then the *Journal*. In 1841 he was appointed Vice-Secretary to the Society.

One of his specialities was the identification of plants sent back by the Society's collectors. From the 1820s to the 1840s, the Society sent emissaries to every continent to discover new plants of potential garden interest. Among them were John Damper Parks, who introduced yellow roses from China; Theodor Hartweg, who brought back the ancestors of the modern fuchsia from Mexico; Robert Fortune, who made his first expedition to China for the Society; and best known of all, David Douglas, after whom the Douglas fir was named. Lindley's work on the plants these explorers sent back resulted in a wide range of new plant names being coined. Some of the plants are illustrated in the following pages.

His work for the Society did not prevent Lindley from accepting a range of duties elsewhere. At the age of twenty-nine he was elected Professor of Botany at the newly founded University of London, a post he held for over thirty years. From 1835 to 1853 he was also Professor of Botany to the Society of Apothecaries, a role which brought with it the responsibility of being director of the Chelsea Physic Garden.

Lindley's name as an horticultural editor grew through work outside the Society. From late in 1827 until 1830, he edited the *Pomological Magazine*, a fruit journal modelled in format on Curtis's *Botanical Magazine*. In 1815, Sydenham Edwards, a former artist for Curtis, had started a rival magazine called the *Botanical Register*, and Lindley became its editor in 1829. One of the earliest published accounts of Australian plants, Lindley's important 'Sketch of the vegetation of the Swan River [an Australian colony]' appeared in this magazine in 1839. Then, together with Joseph Paxton, he founded the *Gardeners' Chronicle* in 1841 and *Paxton's Flower Garden* (three volumes, 1850–1853). The former became the longest-running horticultural periodical, and Lindley remained editor until his death.

Lindley's spectacular energy and enthusiasm involved him in further extra-curricular activities. In 1838 he compiled a report on the condition of the royal gardens at Kew, which led to the establishment of the Royal Botanic Gardens, of which his old friend William Hooker was made the first Director. He was also active on the 1845 commission to enquire into the causes of the Irish potato blight; a juror for food products at the Great Exhibition of 1851; and for many years he was consulted by the Admiralty about the planting of the island of Ascension.

Lindley's great passion for the family of the Orchidaceae began with his work for William Cattley, after whom he named the genus *Cattleya*. He was the first botanist to work out a classification of orchids, and wrote prolifically on the subject, his most notable works being the *Sertum orchidaceum* (1838) and *The Genera and Species of Orchidaceous Plants* (1830–1840). He coined the names of approximately eighty orchid genera still recognised today, including *Cattleya*, *Coelogyne*, *Laelia*, *Lycaste* and *Miltonia*. He has been called the father of modern orchidology, and the American Orchid Society named its scientific journal *Lindleyana* in his honour.

Among his numerous other works were: *Rosarum monographia* (1820); *Digitalium monographia* (1821); *Synopsis of the British Flora* (1829); *Introduction to the Natural System of Botany* (1830); *Fossil Flora of Great Britain* with William Hutton (1831–1837), long the standard work in English; *Ladies' Botany* (1834); *Key to Structural and Systematic Botany* (1835); the text for the last volumes of Sibthorp's *Flora Graeca* (1835–37); *Victoria Regia* (1837); *Flora Medica* (1838); *Theory of Horticulture* (1840); *Elements of Botany* (1841); *The Vegetable Kingdom* (1846); and the initial botanical text for E. J. Ravenscroft's

*Pinetum Britannicum* (1863).

In 1858 Lindley was finally promoted to Secretary of the Society. He held the office during the period when its name was changed to the Royal Horticultural Society. Failing health brought his contribution to public life to an end after he helped organize the Great Exhibition of 1862. This sequel to the exhibition of 1851 was held in the RHS's new gardens in Kensington. A public subscription was raised for him, and E.V. Eddis painted his portrait, which now hangs in the library named after him. After an incredibly full life, his last years were spent suffering from a failing memory and 'softening of the brain'; he died on 31 October 1865.

Lindley left an unintended double legacy to the world. He married in 1823 and had three children, and for several years the Lindley family lived at Bedford House, Acton, near the Society's garden. After his death, this estate became the site of London's first garden suburb, Bedford Park, the course of whose streets was planned in order to preserve as many of Lindley's trees as possible.

His second legacy was the Lindley Library. In 1859 the Horticultural Society sold its library during a period of financial retrenchment. When it could afford to begin to replace this loss, using profits from the International Botanical Congress and Horticultural Exhibition, the Society purchased Lindley's personal library to serve as the nucleus of a new collection. In 1868, the library was invested in the Lindley Library Trust (which is now administered by the RHS as sole Trustee) in order to ensure that it could never be sold again. Lindley's acquisitions now form the cornerstone of the world's greatest horticultural library.

Of the plants named after Lindley, the following are still available from British nurseries: *Aeonium lindleyi*, *Buddleja lindleyana*, *Corydalis lindleyana*, *Photinia lindleyana*, *Rhododendron lindleyi* and *Salix lindleyana*. There are other plants currently available that were once named after Lindley, but which are now known by other names: *Bignonia lindleyana* (now *Clytostoma callistegioides*) and *Sorbaria lindleyana*, (now *S. tomentosa*).

Brent Elliott
The Royal Horticultural Society

# A

Jill + Rosie Aitken.
2. Hawthorne Place.
Blairgowrie
PH 10 6UP.

01250 - 876090.

*Rosa macrophylla*, a hand-coloured engraving after a drawing by John Lindley
from his *Rosarum monographia* (1820)

# B

SHEILA + BOB BAIRD
15 STEPPING STONES,
BIDFORD ON AVON
B50 4 PH.

01789 - 491645.
DEBBIE BAIRD.
68 GREENHILL, EVESHAM
WR11 4NF, WORCS.

01386 - 446043

MAGGIE + GERRY BYRNE
11 WINNERSH GATE
WINNERSH WOKINGHAM.
RG 41 5PL.

*Clematis lanuginosa*, a hand-retouched chromolithograph by Louis-Aristide-Léon Constans
(*fl.* 1830s–1860s), from the third volume of *Paxton's Flower Garden* (1852–1853) by John Lindley
and Joseph Paxton. This species had first flowered in cultivation that year, in the nursery of
Standish and Noble.

*A*

*Dendrobium caerulescens* (now *D. nobile*), a hand-coloured engraving after a drawing by Miss S. A. Drake (*fl.* 1820s–1840s), from John Lindley's *Sertum orchidaceum* (1838–1841)

Now known as *Encyclia vitellina*, this orchid was named *Epidendrum vitellinum* by John Lindley. The hand-coloured engraving after a drawing by Miss S. A. Drake (*fl.* 1820s–1840s), is from Lindley's *Sertum orchidaceum* (1838–1841).

B

# C

Pam + Tony Churchward,
4 Sackville Lane,
East Grinstead,
RH19 2 AU  W. Sussex.

*Papaver bracteatum*, a hand-coloured engraving from John Lindley's *Collectanea botanica* (1821), of a plant both named and drawn by Lindley

*Hibiscus syriacus* var. *chinensis*, a hand-retouched chromolithograph by Louis-Aristide-Léon Constans (*fl.* 1830s–1860s), from the third volume of *Paxton's Flower Garden* (1852–1853) by John Lindley and Joseph Paxton

C

C

# D

SHIRLEY + ROBERT DUFFY
6 ORLOCK LANE,
GROOMSPORT CO. DOWN
BT 19 6 LS.

028 - 918 - 83191.

*Forsythia viridissima*, an unsigned chromolithograph from the second volume of *Jardin Fleuriste* (1851–1852) by Charles Lemaire, whose principal artist was Jean-Christophe Heyland (1792–1866). This plant was named and described by John Lindley in 1847.

*Portulaca thellusonii*, a hand-coloured engraving after a drawing by Miss S. A. Drake
(*fl.* 1820s–1840s), from the 26th volume of the *Botanical Register* (1840), edited by John Lindley.
This plant was named by Lindley.

# E

HILDA ERVINE.
12 LOUGH ROAD.
CLUNTAGH CROSSGAR.
BT 30 9 LB.

MANDY EASWNG.
P.O. BOX 668.
McLAREN VALE S.A. 5159
(51 OAKLEY ROAD)

00- 61 - 8 - 8383 - 0560.

*Allium caeruleum*, a hand-coloured engraving after a drawing by Miss S. A. Drake
(*fl.* 1820s–1840s), from the 26th volume of the *Botanical Register* (1840), edited by John Lindley

*Iris alata* (now *planifolia*), a hand-coloured engraving after a drawing by Miss
S. A. Drake (*fl.* 1820s–1840s), from the 22nd volume of the *Botanical Register*
(1836), edited by John Lindley

*F*

. Now know as *Bromelia antiacantha*, this plant was named *B. fastuosa* by John Lindley. The hand-coloured engraving after a drawing by Lindley is from his *Collectanea botanica* (1821).

Now known as *Kennedia prostrata*, this plant was named *K. maryattae* by John Lindley. The hand-coloured engraving, after a drawing by Miss S. A. Drake (*fl.* 1820s–1840s), was published in the 21st volume of the *Botanical Register* (1836), edited by Lindley.

# G

The 'Common Muscadine' grape, a hand-coloured engraving after a drawing by Augusta Innes Withers (1792–1869), from the first volume of John Lindley's *Pomological Magazine* (1827–1828)

*Clematis florida* 'Bicolor', a hand-coloured engraving after a drawing by Miss S. A. Drake (*fl.* 1820s–1840s), from the 24th volume of the *Botanical Register* (1838), edited by John Lindley

# H

Jan + John Henery
23 Manning Street.
Stansbury S.A 5582.

Janne Hofftilley.
Il Castillo
16. Brancanno
50236 Pieve Santo Stefano
Arezzo    Italy.
Residence Isgran 2000.
# 202.
Val d'Isere
France.

Leo + Lin Hayes.

*Catasetum atratum*, a hand-coloured engraving after a drawing by Miss S. A. Drake (*fl.* 1820s–1840s), from the 24th volume of the *Botanical Register* (1838), edited by John Lindley. This plant was named by Lindley.

*Mimulus cardinalis*, a hand-coloured engraving, after a drawing by Miss S. A. Drake (*fl.* 1820s–1840s), from the *Transactions of the Horticultural Society* (1835). The plant was discovered and named by the Horticultural Society's collector David Douglas, and John Lindley published the first description.

# I

*Odontoglossum laeve*, a chromolithograph after a drawing by Walter Hood Fitch (1817–1892) of an orchid named by John Lindley and published in James Bateman's *Monograph of Odontoglossum* (1874)

*Mucuna pruriens*, a hand-coloured engraving after a drawing by Miss S. A. Drake (*fl.* 1820s–1840s), from the 24th volume of the *Botanical Register* (1838), edited by John Lindley

# J

Susie + Chris Jones
51. Picksley Crescent
Holton - le - Clay
Grimsby DN36 5DR.
Lincs.

*Oxyramphis* (now *Lespedeza*) *macrostyla*, a hand-coloured engraving after a drawing by Miss S. A. Drake (*fl.* 1820s–1840s), from the 32nd volume of the *Botanical Register* (1846), edited by John Lindley. This plant was introduced into England through the Horticultural Society in 1845.

*J*

*Passiflora* × *caeruleoracemosa* (now *P.* × *violacea*), the first hybrid passion flower; a hand-coloured engraving after a drawing by John Lindley, from the *Transactions of the Horticultural Society* (1820)

# K

| | |
|---|---|
| JOYCE KAYE. 5. CHAPMAN AVENUE, MC LAREN VALE S.A 5171 | |
| JEREMY KAYE. + GAYE 9. FOREST AVENUE, BLACKFOREST SA.5035 ADELAIDE. | 00 - 61 - 8 - 8297 -8729 |
| DUNCAN KAYE + COLINE 55 EMERALD STREET, FLAGSTAFF HILL SA5159 ADELAIDE. | 00 - 61 - 8 - mob: 0418902855 ⒟ 0404 - 128476 . |
| JOYCE KAYE 36/91 MAIN ROAD MC LAREN VALE S.A 5171. | 00 - 61 - 8 - 8323-9283 . |

*Sollya linearis*, a hand-coloured engraving after a drawing by Miss S. A. Drake (*fl.* 1820s–1840s), from the 26th volume of the *Botanical Register* (1840), edited by John Lindley, who also named the plant

K

*Berberis nepalensis* (now *vulgaris*), a hand-retouched chromolithograph by
Louis-Aristide-Léon Constans (*fl.* 1830s–1860s), from the third volume of
*Paxton's Flower Garden* (1852–1853) by John Lindley and Joseph Paxton

# L

GLENNIE LANGILLE
P.O. BOX 613.
PICTOU. BOK 1 HD.
NOVA SCOTIA.
CANADA.

*Rosa sulphurea* (now *R. hemisphaerica*), a hand-coloured engraving after a drawing by John Curtis (1791–1862), from John Lindley's *Rosarum monographia* (1820)

L

*Garrya elliptica*, a hand-coloured engraving after a drawing by Miss S. A. Drake (*fl.* 1820s–1840s), from the 20th volume of the *Botanical Register* (1834–1835), edited by John Lindley. This plant was discovered by the Horticultural Society's collector David Douglas and first described by Lindley.

$\mathcal{L}$

# M

DIED FANNI MARR.
14 BELMONT PARK,
BELFAST  BT4 3JU.
Co. DOWN.

FANNI MARR.
MILLEN BAY ROAD
PORTAFERRY Co. DOWN

DIED 028 - 906 - 53305.
WILFORD McFARLANE.
45 ARDMORE ROAD.
CRUMLIN. CO. ANTRIM.
BT29 4 QT.

028 - 427 - 28515.

McLAREN VALE FLORIST.
MAIN ROAD
McLAREN VALE.

00 - 61 - 8 - 8323 - 8555.

*Cattleya loddigesii*, a hand-coloured engraving after a drawing by John Lindley, from his *Collectanea botanica* (1821). Both the genus and the species were named by Lindley.

*M*

*Primula sinensis*, a hand-coloured engraving from John Lindley's *Collectanea botanica* (1821) of a plant both named and drawn by Lindley

*Tacsonia* (now *Passiflora*) *manicata*, a hand-retouched chromolithograph by Louis-Aristide-Léon Constans (*fl.* 1830s–1860s), from the first volume of *Paxton's Flower Garden* (1850–1851) by John Lindley and Joseph Paxton

*Amaryllis solandraeflora* (now *Hippeastrum solandraeflorum*), a hand-coloured engraving from John Lindley's *Collectanea botanica* (1821), of a plant both named and drawn by Lindley (from William Cattley's specimen)

# O

Gooseberry 'Crompton's Sheba Queen', a hand-coloured engraving after a drawing by Augusta Innes Withers (1792–1869), from the first volume of John Lindley's *Pomological Magazine* (1827–1828)

O

*Amaryllis vittata major,* now classified as a form of *Hippeastrum vittatum,* a hand-coloured engraving after a drawing by John Lindley from his *Collectanea botanica* (1821)

# *PQ*

ALAN + AILEEN PINKERTON
11 HAZELDENE PARK.
BANGOR BT 20 5 LD.
CO. DOWN    N. IRELAND.

028-914-665877
BABS PINKERTON.
33 WAVERLEY DRIVE
BANGOR BT 20 5 LD.
CO. DOWN    N. IRELAND.

*Camellia reticulata*, a hand-coloured engraving after a drawing by Alfred Chandler (1804–1896), from *Illustrations and Descriptions of the Plants which Compose the Natural Order Camellieae* (1831) by Chandler and William Beattie Booth. This plant was introduced into England by the Horticultural Society's collector John Damper Parks in 1824 and was named by John Lindley.

*Disa grandiflora*, a hand-coloured engraving after a drawing by Miss S. A. Drake (*fl.* 1820s–1840s), from John Lindley's *Sertum orchidaceum* (1838–1841)

# R

BETTY + DAVID RODGERS
17 COACH HOUSE AVENUE,
NOVAR GARDEN
S.A          ADELAIDE.

BETTY + DAVID RODGERS
140/91 MAIN ROAD,
McLAREN VALE
SA 5171.

The 'deep blood-coloured moutan' (a variety of *Paeonia suffruticosa*), a hand-retouched chromolithograph by Louis-Aristide-Léon Constans (*fl.* 1830s–1860s), from the first volume of *Paxton's Flower Garden* (1850–1851) by John Lindley and Joseph Paxton

*Anemone japonica*, a hand-coloured engraving after a drawing by Miss S. A. Drake (*fl.* 1820s–1840s), from the 31st volume of the *Botanical Register* (1845), edited by John Lindley. Although described in the 18th century, it was not grown in England until Robert Fortune introduced it through the Horticultural Society in 1844.

# S

*Rosa woodsii*, an original drawing in watercolour by John Lindley, dated 1821. Lindley named this species in 1820 from a specimen from the Missouri River area.

S

*Digitalis ambigua* (now *grandiflora*), a hand-coloured engraving after a drawing by Ferdinand Bauer (1760–1826), from John Lindley's *Digitalium monographia* (1821)

# *T*

The graft-hybrid + *Laburnocytisus* 'Adami', a hand-coloured engraving after a drawing by Miss S. A. Drake ( *fl.* 1820s–1840s), from the 23rd volume of the *Botanical Register* (1837), edited by John Lindley

T

*T*

*Helleborus atrorubens*, a hand-retouched chromolithograph by Louis-Aristide-Léon Constans (*fl.* 1830s–1860s), from the third volume of *Paxton's Flower Garden* (1852–1853) by John Lindley and Joseph Paxton

# UV

Mrs. J.F. Verner.
Room 15 River House.
131 Central Promenade
Newcastle BT33 0EU
028 - 437 24138
Mr. Peter Verner.
3562. Joan Drive
Mississauga L5B 1T8.
Ontario. Canada.

The 'Turkey' apricot, a hand-coloured engraving after a drawing by Augusta Innes Withers (1792–1869), from the first volume of John Lindley's *Pomological Magazine* (1827–1828)

Varieties of *Tulipa scabriscapa*, a hand-coloured engraving after a drawing by Miss S. A. Drake (*fl.* 1820s–1840s), from the 23rd volume of the *Botanical Register* (1837), edited by John Lindley

# W

EDMOND WEAVING.
62 WEST STREET
CARSHALTON SM5 2PR.
SURREY.

The 'Barnet' raspberry, a hand-coloured engraving after a drawing by Augusta Innes Withers (1792–1869), from the first volume of John Lindley's *Pomological Magazine* (1827–1828)

W

# W

*Astrapaea wallichii*, a hand-coloured engraving after a drawing by John Lindley from his *Collectanea botanica* (1821)

# XYZ

*Brownea ariza*, the Ariza plant, a hand-retouched chromolithograph by Louis-Aristide-Léon Constans (*fl.* 1830s–1860s), from the second volume of *Paxton's Flower Garden* (1851–1852) by John Lindley and Joseph Paxton. The plant was collected by Theodor Hartweg for the Horticultural Society.

*Canna speciosa* (now *C. coccinea*), a hand-coloured engraving by M. Hart, from the 15th volume of the *Botanical Register* (1829), the first volume to be edited by John Lindley

# NOTES